LifePrints
ESL FOR ADULTS

Literacy

MaryAnn Cunningham Florez

New Readers Press

LifePrints Literacy
1-56420-236-4
Copyright © 2002

New Readers Press
U.S. Publishing Division of Laubach Literacy
1320 Jamesville Ave., Syracuse, New York 13210

Printed in the United States of America
9 8 7 6 5 4 3 2 1

Acquisitions Editor: Paula L. Schlusberg
Copy Editor: Judi Lauber
Production Director: Heather Witt
Designer: Shelagh Clancy
Cover Designer: Kimbrly Koennecke
Illustrators: Linda Tiff, Luciana Mallozzi, James P. Wallace, Adam Schickling
Cover Illustrator: James P. Wallace
Production Specialist: Alexander Jones

Series development: Robert Ventre, Inc.
                       Course Crafters, Inc.

Table of Contents

 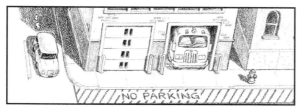

1·2·3·4·5·6
Welcome to English Class ■ ■ ■ ■ ■

WELCOME TO ENGLISH CLASS.

LISTEN. READ.

WELCOME TO ENGLISH CLASS.

THANK YOU.

MY NAME IS SUSAN.

MY NAME IS ALEX.

TRACE.

<u>S U S A N</u>

<u>A L E X</u>

The Alphabet

LISTEN. SAY.

TRACE. WRITE.

A A A A A

B B B B B

C C C C C

D D D D D

E E E E E

F F F F F

G G G G G

H H H H H

I I I I I

J J J J J

K K K K K

L L L L L

M M M M M

N N N N N

O O O O O

P P P P P

Q Q Q Q Q

R R R R R

S S S S S

T T T T T

U U U U U

V V V V V

W W W W W

X X X X X

Y Y Y Y Y

Z Z Z Z Z

CIRCLE THE WORD.

1.	E	ALEX	NAME	⬭ENGLISH
2.	S	CLASS	SUSAN	WELCOME
3.	N	ENGLISH	CLASS	NAME
4.	W	WELCOME	ALEX	SUSAN
5.	A	NAME	ALEX	CLASS

  LISTEN. CIRCLE THE WORD.

1.	NAME	THANK	ALEX
2.	WELCOME	CLASS	SUSAN
3.	ALEX	ENGLISH	NAME
4.	SUSAN	ALEX	CLASS
5.	WELCOME	MY	THANK

READ. WRITE YOUR NAME.

MY NAME IS SUSAN.

MY NAME IS ALEX.

MY NAME IS

_____.

READ. WRITE THE WORDS.

BOARD

——————

TEACHER

——————

STUDENT

——————

PEN

——————

PENCIL

——————

BOOK

——————

PAPER

——————

Ⓐ CIRCLE THE LETTER.

1. (D)ESK	H	Y	T	D
2. (C)HAIR	M	C	G	O
3. (T)EACHER	T	W	J	O
4. (B)OOK	P	X	B	D
5. (P)ENCIL	K	P	R	Y

⬛ MATCH.

BOARD

PEN

1.  PAPER

STUDENT

2.

DESK

3.

PENCIL

4.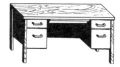

5.

6.

A **WRITE THE NAMES.**

MY NAME _____

MY TEACHER _____

A **WRITE THE LETTERS. CHECK.**

		MY CLASS	
		YES	NO
	_ E S _		
	_ H _ I R		
	P _ P _ _		

1·2·3·4·5·6
Personal Information

LISTEN. READ THE STORY.

HELLO.

MY NAME IS <u>ALEX MARCOS</u>.

MY FIRST NAME IS <u>ALEX</u>.

MY LAST NAME IS <u>MARCOS</u>.

MEXICO

I AM FROM <u>MEXICO</u>.

 WRITE THE NAMES.

1. NAME <u>A̲̱_____ M̲̱_____</u>

2. FIRST NAME <u>A̲̱_____</u>

3. LAST NAME <u>M̲̱_____</u>

LISTEN. READ THE STORY.

 WRITE THE NAMES.

MY NAME IS SUSAN DAVIS.

MY FIRST NAME IS _____.

MY LAST NAME IS _____.

I AM FROM THE UNITED STATES.

I AM MARRIED.

I HAVE 2 CHILDREN.

I HAVE <u>2</u> CHILDREN.   I HAVE <u>1</u> CHILD.

 SAY.

  TRACE. WRITE.

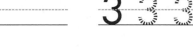

0 0 0

3 3 3

1 1 1

4 4 4

2 2 2

5 5 5

MATCH.

1. 2

2. 5

3. 3

4. 4

  LISTEN. CIRCLE THE NUMBER.

1.	3	5	1	0
2.	5	2	4	3
3.	4	2	5	3
4.	0	4	3	1

The Family

👁️🗣️ **LOOK. SAY THE WORD.**

✏️ **WRITE THE WORD.**

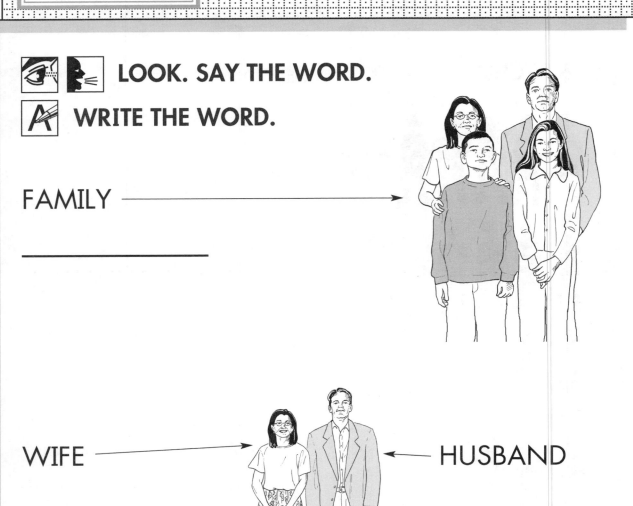

FAMILY ⟶

_____

WIFE ⟶   ⟵ HUSBAND

_____   _____

PARENTS ⟶   ⟵ CHILDREN

_____   _____

LOOK. SAY THE WORD.

WRITE THE WORD.

MOTHER

_____

SON

_____

DAUGHTER

_____

FATHER

_____

SON

_____

DAUGHTER

_____

BROTHER

_____

SISTER

_____

Brothers and Sisters

 WRITE THE NUMBER.

I AM SINGLE.

I HAVE ___ CHILDREN.

I HAVE ___ BROTHERS.

I HAVE ___ SISTER.

I HAVE ___ MOTHER.

I HAVE ___ FATHER.

Ⓐ CIRCLE.

1. WIFE	🧍	(🧍)
2. FATHER	🧍	🧍
3. SON	🧍	🧍
4. DAUGHTER	🧍	🧍
5. BROTHER	🧍	🧍
6. MOTHER	🧍	🧍

 LISTEN.

Ⓐ CIRCLE THE LETTER THAT BEGINS THE WORDS.

1.	P	M	T	N
2.	R	X	B	S
3.	W	D	A	B
4.	F	K	V	G

A **WRITE YOUR STORY.**

MY NAME IS _____.

MY FIRST NAME IS _____.

MY LAST NAME IS _____.

I AM FROM _____.

I AM _____.

I HAVE _____ CHILD

I HAVE _____ BROTHER

I HAVE _____ SISTER

1·2·3·4·5·6

In the Neighborhood

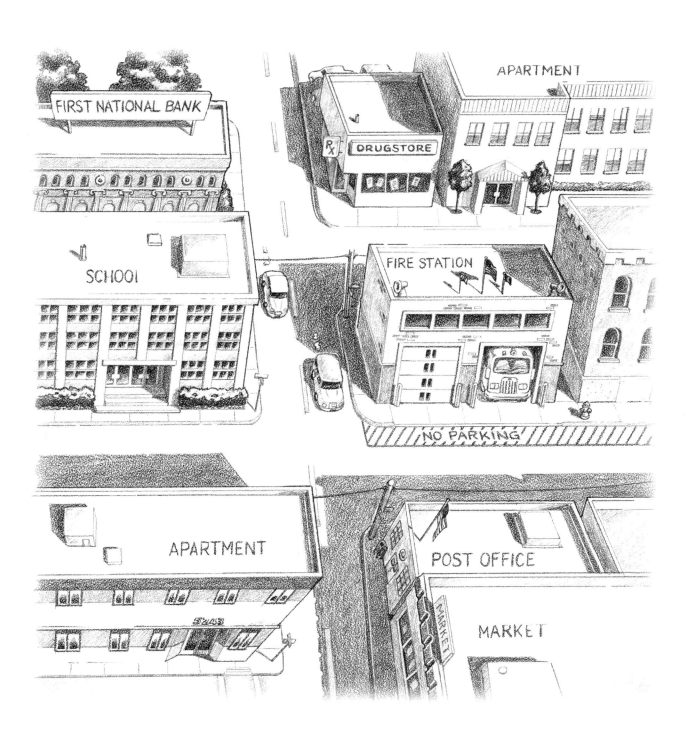

Alex Lives Here

 Listen.

Alex lives at 5243 Walnut Street.

Trace.

1. Name: <u>Alex Marcos</u>

2. Address: <u>5243 Walnut Street</u>

Write the address.

1. _2134_ Walnut Street

2. _____ State Avenue

3. _____ River Road

4. 411 _State Avenue_

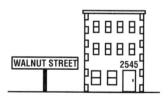

5. 2545 _____

6. 3253 _____

Places in the Neighborhood

 Match.

1.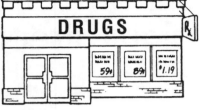

2.

3.

4.

5.

6.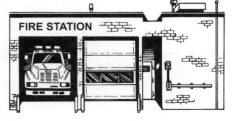

post office

supermarket

drugstore

fire station

school

bank

Yes   No

 Circle the signs.

Match.

1.

2.

3.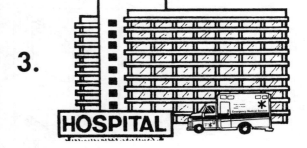

Write the words.

1. policestation _____ _____

2. firestation _____ _____

3. postoffice _____ _____

 A **Say the number. Write the number.**

0 000

5 555

1 111

6 666

2 222

7 777

3 333

8 888

4 444

9 999

On the Phone

  Read. Write.

 telephone

 telephone number
(713) 398-2746

 My telephone number

(____) ____ - _____

  Listen to the number. Circle Yes or No.

1. 398-2746	Yes	No
2. 332-5168	Yes	No
3. 947-4318	Yes	No

Listen.

  Trace. Write.

My name is

Alex Marcos .

My telephone number is

(713) 691-8896 .

My name is

_____ .

My telephone number is

(713) _____ .

My name is

_____ .

My telephone number is

_____ .

Write.

Information

Personal Information

Name_____

Address_____

_____

Telephone Number_____

Emergency Information

Emergency Number_____

Fire_____

Police_____

Hospital_____

1·2·3·4·5·6

Going Shopping ■ ■ ■ ■ ■ ■ ■ ■

Listen.

I shop on Saturday.
When?

_____ day.

 Circle the day.

When?

Sunday	Monday	Tuesday	Wednesday	Thursday	Friday	Saturday
		1	2	3	4	5
6	7	8	9	10	11	12
13	14	15	16	17	18	19
20	21	22	23	24	25	26
27	28	29	30			

Write the day. Say the day.

1. _Sun_ day

2. _Mon_ day

3. _ _ _ _ _ day

4. _ _ _ _ _ _ day

5. _ _ _ _ _ _ day

6. _ _ _ day

7. _ _ _ _ _ _ day

  Listen. Write the days.

When?

 1. _____ and

_____.

 2. _____ and

_____.

Numbers 10–49

 Trace. Write.

10 _10_	20 _20_	3_0_	4_0_
11 _11_	21 _21_	3_1_	4__
12 _12_	22 _22_	3_2_	4__
13 _13_	23 _23_	3__	4__
14 _14_	24 _24_	3__	
15 _15_	25 _25_	___	___
16 _16_	26 _26_	___	___
17 _17_	27 _27_	___	___
18 _18_	28 _28_	___	___
19 _19_	29 _29_	___	___

Listen.

I shop at the supermarket.
Where?
The _____.

 Circle the word.

1. post office
supermarket
bank

2. drugstore
school
fire station

I shop for food.

A Write the word.

1.

_____

2.

_____

3.

_____

4.

_____

5.

_____

6.

_____

Listen.

How much?

$3.20

$3.00 and $.20

 **Match.**

1.

$10.00

$20.00

$1.00

$5.00

2.

3.

4.

Match.

1. $.10

2. $.25

3. $.05

4. $.01

How much? Write.

1. $___ .46

3. $10.___

2. $___ .09

4. $___.___

Circle the money to pay the bill.

Martin's Supermarket

Bread............ $1.15
Milk............. $2.00
Eggs............. $1.30
Chicken........$3.00

TOTAL: $7.45

  Listen. Circle the price.

How much?

1. $3.00 $5.00

2. $8.16 $8.12

3. $12.25 $20.25

4. $40.00 $14.00

5. $39.00 $.39

I Shop on Friday

  Listen. Read the story.

 I shop on Friday.

 I shop at the supermarket.

 I shop for chicken, bread, and milk.

 $24.19, please.

 Write about the story.

1. When? _____

2. Where? _____

3. How much? _____

1·2·3·4·5·6

I Am Sick ■ ■ ■ ■ ■ ■ ■ ■ ■

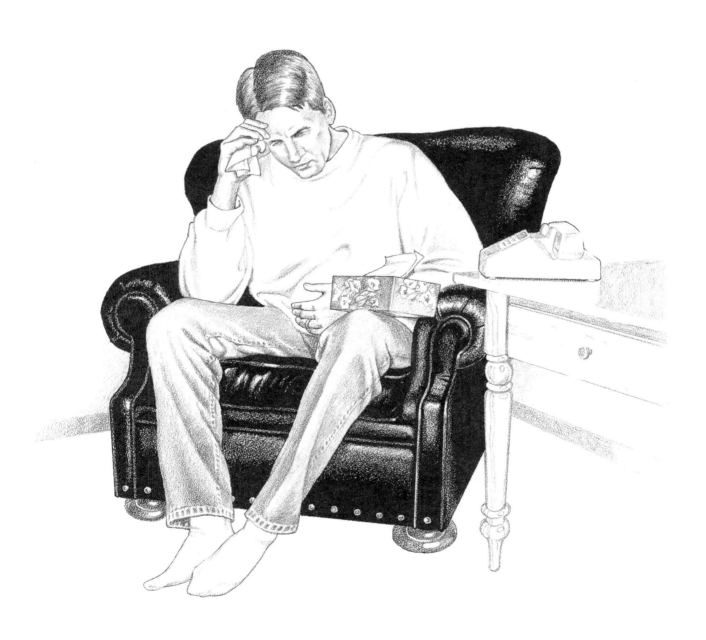

Listen. Read the conversation.

Hello. Dr. Smith's office.

Hello. I am sick.

What's wrong?

My stomach hurts.
My head hurts.
I have a fever.

Listen. Write the word.

1. eye	**4.** nose	**7.** stomach	**10.** hand
2. head	**5.** throat	**8.** arm	**11.** leg
3. ear	**6.** chest	**9.** back	**12.** foot

1. _____

4. _____

5. _____

6. _____

7. _____

2. _____

3. _____

8. _____

9. _____

10. _____

11. _____

12. _____

Match.

1.   ear

2.   arm

3.   foot

4.   hand

5.   eyes

  Listen. Circle the word that rhymes.

1.	dead	leg	head
2.	tack	back	stomach
3.	fear	ear	foot
4.	sand	hand	head

Write the words.

1. My _____head_____ hurts.

2. My _____ hurts.

3. My _____ _____.

4. I _____have_____ a fever.

5. I _____ a cough.

6. I _____ a runny nose.

Listen. Read the conversation.

Hello. Dr. Smith's office.	Hello. I am sick.
What's wrong?	My stomach hurts. My head hurts. I have a fever.
Can you come at 3:00?	3:00? Yes. Thank you.

3:00　　　　　3:00　　　　　3:00

 Write the time. Say the time.

 1. _____

 2. _____

 3. _____

 4. _____

 5. _____

 6. _____

 7. _____

 8. _____

 9. _____

 10. _____

 11. _____

 12. _____

What Time Is It?

3:10

3:10

3:10

✏️ Write the time.

 1. _____

 2. _____

 3. _____

 4. _____

 5. _____

 6. _____

 7. _____

 8. _____

Listen to the time. Circle the time.

1. 4:00 4:05 4:14

2. 9:31 9:30 8:30

3. 6:40 6:14 6:45

4. 11:02 11:20 11:12

5. 1:15 1:50 1:05

 Listen. Circle the number.

1. 40 14

2. 60 16

3. 30 13

4. 50 15

5. 20 12

Write the conversation.

 **Say the conversation with a friend.**

Amy: _____. Dr. Smith's office.

Jim: Hello. I am _____.

Amy: What's _____?

Jim: My _____ hurts.

My _____ hurts.

I have a _____.

Amy: Can you come at _____?

Jim: _____? Yes. Thank you.

1·2·3·4·5·6

I Want a Job ■ ■ ■ ■ ■ ■ ■ ■ ■

Listen. Read the story.

My name is Robert Chang.

I want a job.

I read the newspaper.

I talk to friends.

I look for
help wanted signs.

A Write the words.

1. Robert wants a _____.

2. Robert reads the _____.

3. Robert talks to _____.

4. Robert looks for _____

_____ signs.

A Underline what is different.

1. <u>I want</u> a job.   <u>Robert wants</u> a job.

2. I read the newspaper.   Robert reads the newspaper.

3. I talk to friends.   Robert talks to friends.

4. I look for signs.   Robert looks for signs.

You Want a Job

 Listen. Circle the word.

1. want   wants

2. read   reads

3. talk   talks

4. look for   looks for

✔ **You want a job. Check what you do.**

____ **1.** I read the newspaper.

____ **2.** I talk to friends.

____ **3.** I look for help wanted signs.

 ✔ **Ask a friend. Check what your friend does.**

____ **1.** My friend reads the newspaper.

____ **2.** My friend talks to friends.

____ **3.** My friend looks for help wanted signs.

Listen. Read.

 I talk to my friends.

Susan is
a teacher.

Stan is
a waiter.

Alex is a
mechanic.

Kim is a
housecleaner.

Monica is a
salesperson.

John is a
construction
worker.

Match.

1.    salesperson

2.    housecleaner

3.    mechanic

4.    construction worker

5.    waiter

 Write your job.

I am a _____.

HELP WANTED

SALESPERSON
Monday - Friday
1:00 - 5:00
$9.00/hour

Ⓐ **Circle the answer.**

Job	salesperson	housecleaner	teacher
Days	Monday Tuesday Wednesday Thursday	Friday Saturday Sunday	
Hours	1:00–4:00	11:00–6:00	1:00–5:00
Pay	$9.00/hour	$9.00/day	$19.00/hour

A Job Application

 Listen to the conversation.

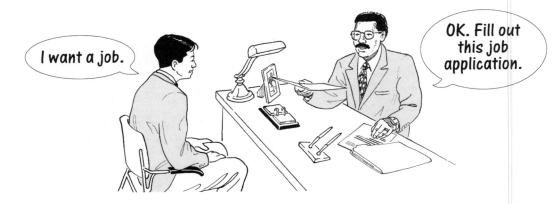

Read.

Name   <u>Robert Chang</u>
First Name   <u>Robert</u>
Last Name   <u>Chang</u>

John M. Chang
1911 North Street
Los Angeles CA 90054

Robert Chang
1634 Walnut St.
Houston, TX 77024

City: <u>Houston</u>   State: <u>Texas (TX)</u>   Zip: <u>77024</u>

 Write your job application.

JOB APPLICATION FORM
(Please Print)

Name _____ _____
      First   Last

Address _____

City _____ State _____ Zip _____

Telephone _____

Job Experience _____

_____

_____

_____

I Am a Salesperson

  Listen. Read the story.

My name is Robert Chang.

I am a salesperson.

I work on Monday, Tuesday, Wednesday, Thursday and Friday.

I work from 1:00 to 5:00.

35% Sale on all watches

A **Write your story.**

My name is _____.

I am _____.

I work on _____

_____.

I work from _____ to _____.